I BRAKE FOR QUAHOGS

I BRAKE FOR QUAHOGS

BY
DON BOUSQUET

Recreation Publications
A Division of Narragansett Graphics, Inc.
Wakefield, Rhode Island

Recreation Publications
A Division of Narragansett Graphics, inc.
82 High Street, Wakefield, Rhode Island 02880
(401) 789-3041

Published and Printed in the United States of America

To the People
of the State of Rhode Island
and Providence Plantations,
such as they are.

ROGER WILLIAMS
FOUNDER OF RHODE ISLAND

HIS BROTHER,
SHERWIN

"HOW MUCH WOULD YOU EXPECT TO PAY FOR
RHODE ISLAND AND PROVIDENCE PLAN-
TATIONS...? WAIT, DON'T ANSWER, BECAUSE
WE'LL ALSO INCLUDE THIS MIRACLE MAIZE
PROCESSOR AND THREE PIECE SET OF
DELUXE STEAK KNIVES... NOW HOW MUCH
WOULD YOU PAY?"

"TODAY, STUDENTS, WE BEGIN OUR DISCUSSION OF THE NEW ENGLAND STATES. WE'LL BE USING THIS MAP KINDLY DONATED BY THE RHODE ISLAND DEPARTMENT OF ECONOMIC DEVELOPMENT...."

FIRST SOLO FLIGHT LINKING
RHODE ISLAND AND THE AZORES
(1978)

BRISTOL, R.I., 80,000 B.C.

" HEY, MOM ... DAD'S HOME AND HE CAUGHT
A SABER-TOOTHED MEATBALL AND PEPPER
GRINDER ! "

"STEROIDS."

IN THE SYMPATHY SECTION
OF THE OCEAN STATE GREETING CARD SHOPPE

NORTH PROVIDENCE ROCK STAR, BOY VINNIE

DON BOUSQUET

OPENING DAY OF TROUT SEASON
BEAVER RIVER, RICHMOND, R.I.
APRIL, 1959

" HOWARD AND I CAN'T FACE ALL THAT BEACH TRAFFIC. WE'VE BEEN SWIMMING IN THE PAWTUXET RIVER FOR OVER THIRTY YEARS AND GOODNESS KNOWS IT HASN'T DONE US ANY HARM... "

MOVING INEXORABLY INTO THE TWENTY-FIRST CENTURY.

THE LATE, LAMENTED BUT TECHNICALLY INNOVATIVE
BLACKSTONE MEANDERING WRAITH ROADSTER
MANUFACTURED IN SOUTH ATTLEBORO, MASS. 1931-1933

EQUIPPED WITH A 78 RPM VICTROLA LOCATED
JUST FORWARD OF THE FIREWALL, THE CAR WOULD
WARN OF POTENTIAL ON-BOARD HAZARDS.

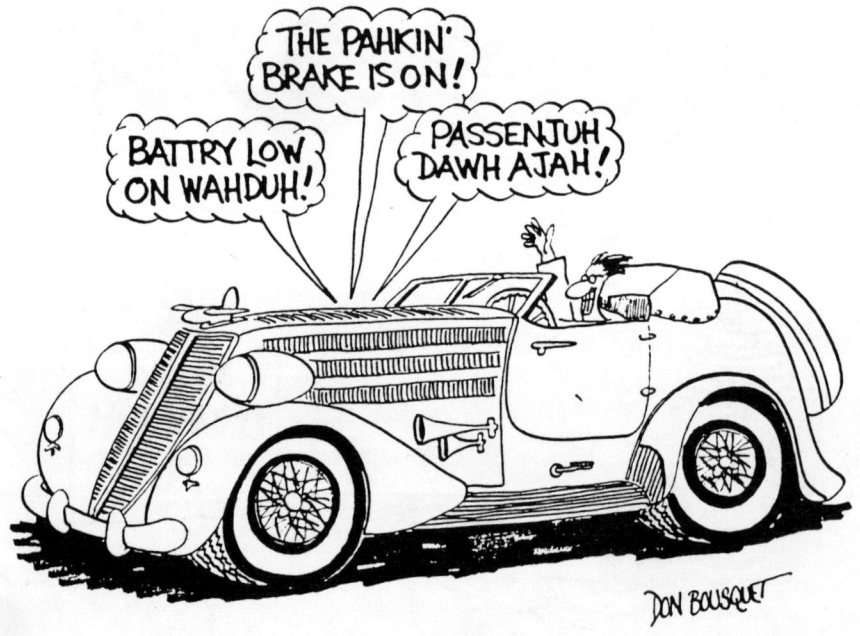

RONALD McDONALD :
THE EARLY YEARS

" OF COURSE, THE BOYS REALLY MISS ALL THE DOINGS HERE IN ROCKVILLE BUT THEY JUST COULDN'T TURN DOWN SUCH A LUCRATIVE CONTRACT WITH THE SLATER PARK ZOO. "

IN THE SPRING OF
1979 DOCTOR BARON VON FRANKENSTEIN
EMIGRATED FROM BAVARIA AND
OPENED A LABORATORY IN
JOHNSTON, RHODE ISLAND.

"☆#¢🪐☀ LIBERALS!"

" IT'S FROM A RECIPE I FOUND IN
THE 'TIMES — IT'S CALLED POACHED
HORSESHOE CRAB 'A LA CREOLE ON A
SHINGLE. "

" THE SPECIAL RADIAL TIRES ON
THIS MODEL WILL GIVE YOU A BETTER
FEEL FOR THE ACTUAL EXPERIENCE
OF DRIVING ON RHODE ISLAND
ROADS. "

SONG AND DANCE MEN FROM
WOONSOCKET

RHODE ISLANDERS IN THE CIVIL WAR

MEN OF THE 2ND R.I. VOLUNTEERS WITH FIXED BULLRAKES, MANASSAS, VA., 1861.

DRAMATIC MOMENTS
IN RHODE ISLAND MEDICINE
No. 52

DOCTOR HEINDRICH GAUCHES OF THE
COMMUNITY COLLEGE OF R.I. SCHOOL OF
NEUROLOGY DISCOVERS A SUBSTANCE TO
COMBAT INSOLENCE AND LONG LINES AT
THE REGISTRY OF MOTOR VEHICLES —
HE CALLS IT, 'GIN'.

NEW
ON THE MENU AT :
Mc DONALD'S of MATUNUCK!

EGG 'N' HORSESHOE CRAB Mc MUFFIN

28

"AT THIS TIME I'D LIKE TO REMIND THE LEARNED COUNSEL FROM HOPE VALLEY THAT HE HAS A NASTY OVER-BITE THERE."

"HAPPY BIRTHDAY, LARRY! IT'S A THREE LAYER DEVIL'S FOOD CLAM CAKE WHIPPED UP BY THE PT. JUDITH FISH-ERMAN'S COOPERATIVE!"

"THIS MONTH'S ISSUE OF 'AMERICAN QUAHOGGER' FEATURES A FULL COLOR CENTERFOLD OF A STAINLESS STEEL TWENTY-EIGHT TOOTH BULLRAKE..."

SURVIVAL TIPS FOR THE
SHIPWRECKED
RHODE ISLANDER

#137 IN A SERIES

DON BOUSQUET

IF DRIFTWOOD IS NOT READILY AVAILABLE
SIMPLY PREPARE A SIGNAL FIRE BY IGNITING
A TWO TO FOUR FOOT PILE OF QUAHOG CHIPS.

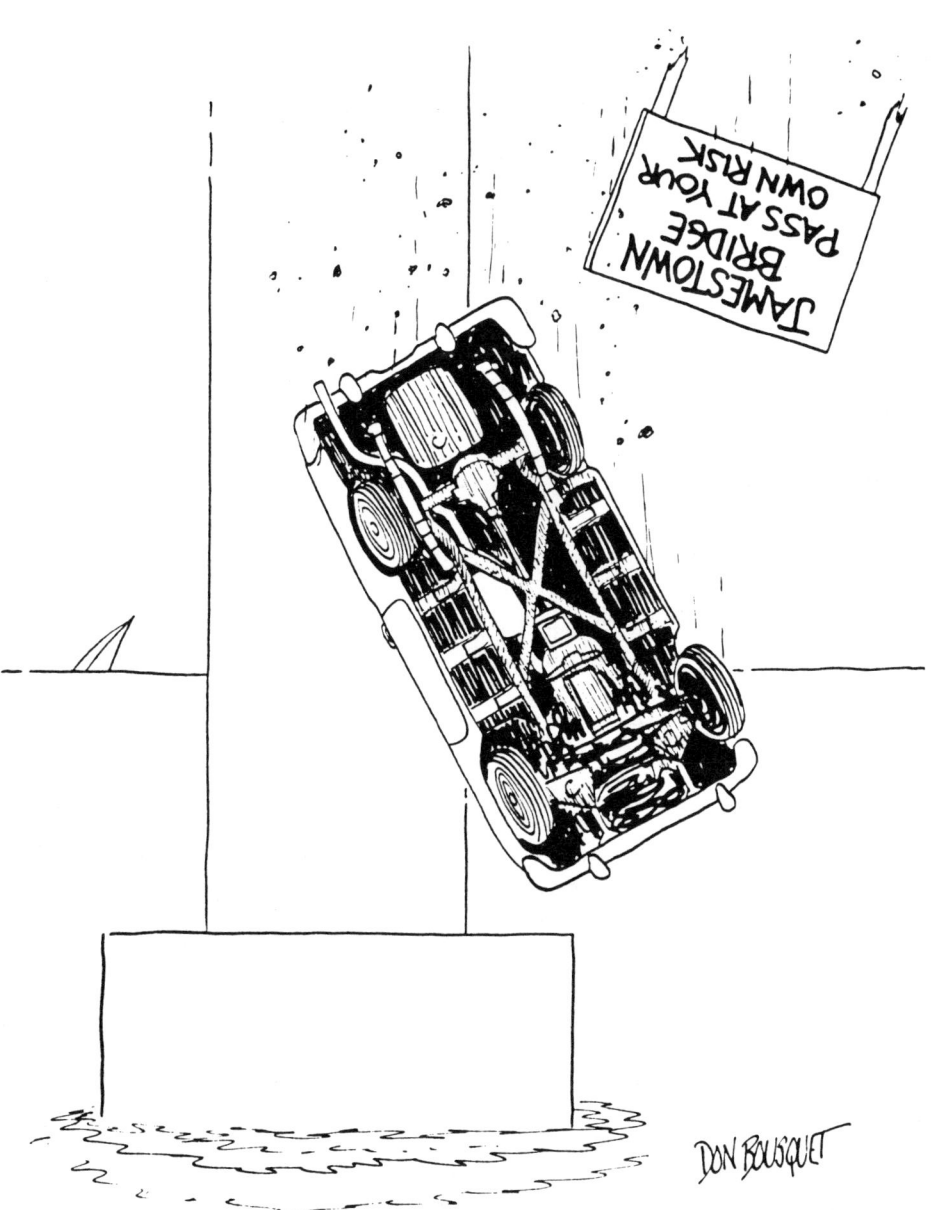

" WE INTERRUPT REGULAR PROGRAMMING FOR
THIS SPECIAL BULLETIN..... THERE WERE NO
RHODE ISLAND OFFICIALS INDICTED FOR
ANYTHING TODAY... DETAILS AT ELEVEN. "

AT THE FIRST-ANNUAL FALL RIVER
CADILLAC WINDSURFING INVITATIONAL
(1984)

38

**RHODE ISLAND
40,000 B.C.**

DON BOUSQUET

FIG. A.

CAVE DRAWING FOUND IN SOUTH
KINGSTOWN DEPICTING AN EARLY
THROWER OF A FRISBEE-LIKE
DEVICE — A LARGE QUAHOG SHELL.

FIG. B.

CAVE DRAWING OF WHAT IS
THOUGHT TO BE AN EARLY
CATCHER OF THAT SAME
FRISBEE-LIKE DEVICE.

REAL RHODE ISLANDER'S CAR

A. ONE LOW BEAM BROKEN, HIGH BEAM MISSING
B. WINDSHIELD PITTED FROM SANDING TRUCKS
C. TWELVE EIGHT-TRACK TAPES (BARRY MANILOW)
D. RIGHT REAR WINDOW INOPERATIVE
E. MOTHER-IN-LAW IN BACK SEAT
F. TRAILER HITCH FOR TOWING QUAHOG SKIFF

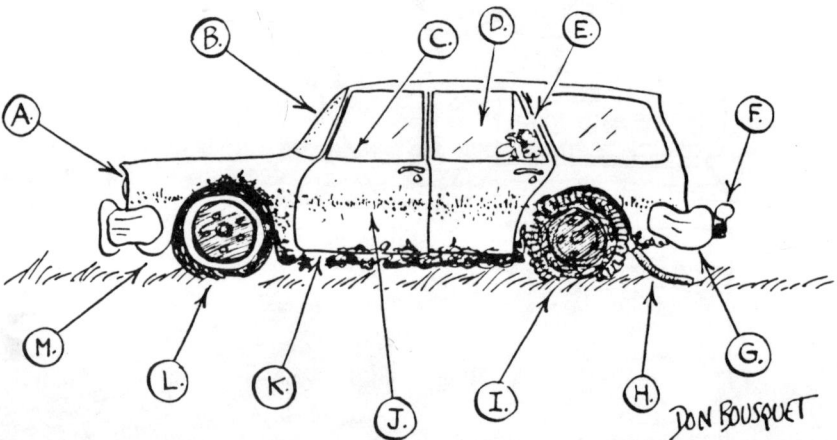

DON BOUSQUET

G. BUMPER STICKER: Hi NEIGHBOR, HAVE A 'GANSETT!
H. EXHAUST PIPE DRAGGING ON GROUND
I. SNOW TIRES... IN JULY
J. 250+ DOOR DINGS FROM ANN & HOPE PARKING LOT
K. BODY ROT, IN A BIG WAY
L. ONE WHITE WALL TIRE, LEFT FRONT
M. FRONT END SHOT

RHODE ISLAND TRAFFIC SIGN

" DON'T JUST SIT THERE! WITH JOE GARRAHY OUT OF THE RACE YOU'VE GOT AS GOOD A CHANCE AS ANYONE TO MAKE ME FIRST LADY OF RHODE ISLAND!"

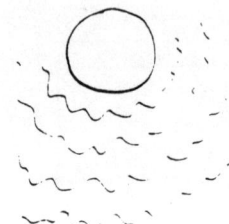

RHODE ISLANDER LOST
IN THE MOJAVE DESERT

DON BOUSQUET

" .... CABINET .... CABINET .... "

" WELL, IT MAY BE COMMERCIALLY VIABLE
BUT I STILL THINK IT'S UNDIGNIFIED... "

" IT WOULD APPEAR, CAPTAIN, THAT WE HAVE BEEN TRANSPORTED BY TIME WARP TO LATE TWENTIETH CENTURY WESTERLY, RHODE ISLAND..."

DUELING QUAHOGGERS

WARWICK POLICE

WEST WARWICK POLICE

" GEE, I'LL BET YOUR GRANDMOTHER
IS THE ONLY LADY IN BARRINGTON
WHO LIKES 'THE A TEAM' AS MUCH
AS WE DO!"

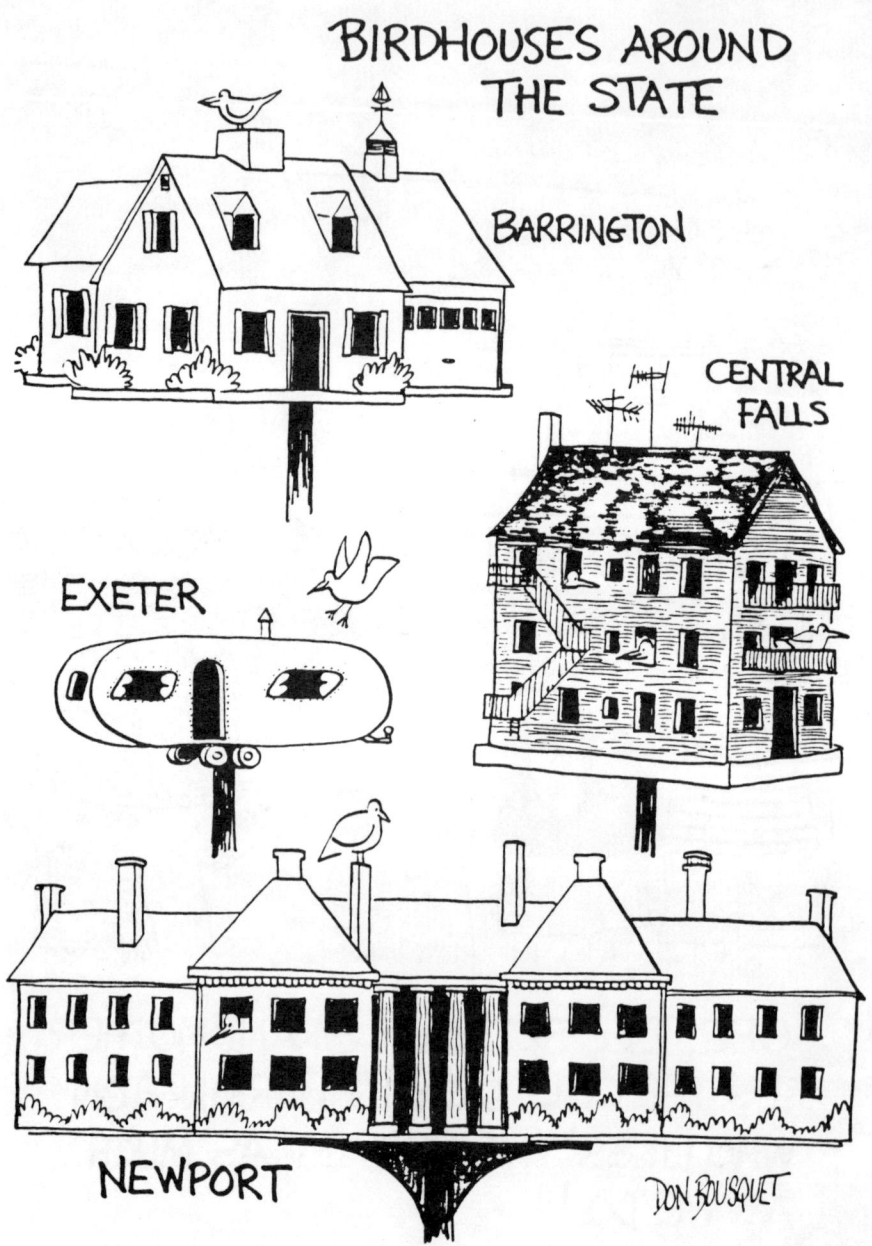

BIRDHOUSES AROUND THE STATE

BARRINGTON

CENTRAL FALLS

EXETER

NEWPORT

DON BOUSQUET

" CHANNEL 36 HAS A NATIONAL GEOGRAPHIC SPECIAL ON THE ODD, NOMADIC MOVEMENTS OF RHODE ISLAND TELEVISION ANCHOR PEOPLE..."

IF JOHN PAUL JONES HAD BEEN FROM WOONSOCKET...

55

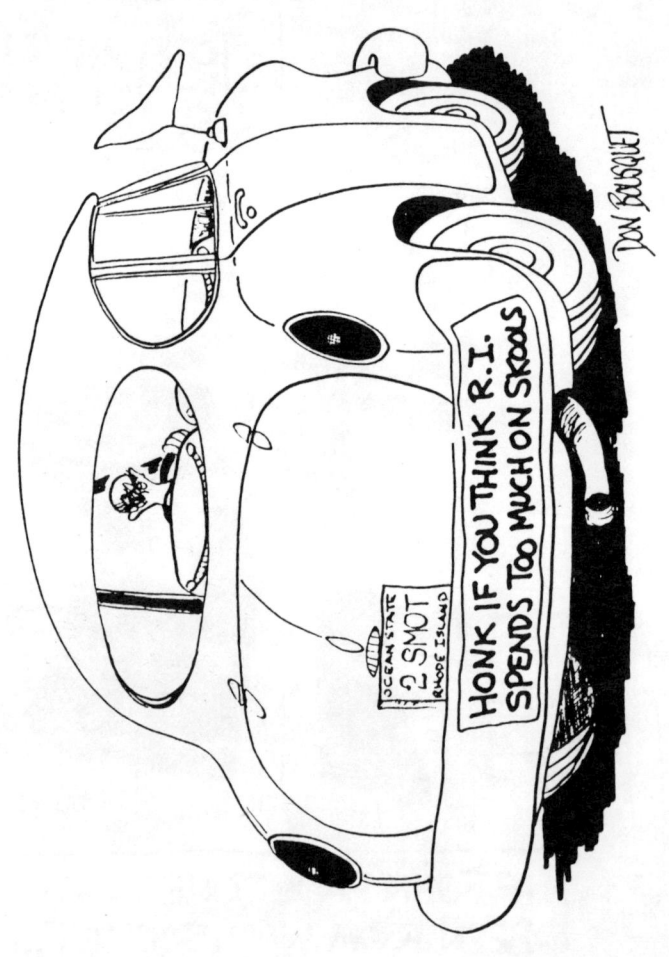

56

"SO THEY MOVED INTO A THREE BED-
ROOM, RAISED RANCH IN PORTSMOUTH
AND, EXCEPT FOR SOME PROBLEMS WITH
THE SEPTIC SYSTEM, LIVED HAPPILY
EVER AFTER... THE END. "

THIS WEEK IN THE
NATIONAL ENQUIRER:

ARE COMMUNIST-BACKED ASPHALT GOPHERS THE _REAL_ CAUSE OF ROAD CONDITIONS IN RHODE ISLAND??

ENQUIRING PEOPLE WANT TO KNOW!

DON BOUSQUET

"GREAT SCOTT! IT APPEARS TO BE AN INVASION OF...OF INTERGALACTIC QUAHOGGERS!"

ARCHE DE GRAMMAR
WOONSOCKET, R.I.

DON BOUSQUET

" WHERE DID YOU COME FROM? WELL, LET'S SEE...
IT WAS FEBRUARY OF '78 AND A GREAT BLIZZARD
HAD INUNDATED THE NORTHEAST. YOUR DADDY AND I
WERE STALLED IN THE BREAK-DOWN LANE OF 95
NORTHBOUND NEAR THE JEFFERSON BLVD. EXIT...
THERE WE WERE, STUCK IN A '72 MATADOR WITH
LOTS OF TIME ON OUR HANDS... "

" IT WAS MAY 31, 1969. I SENT HIM TO THE ALMAC IN WAKEFIELD TO PICK UP TWO POUNDS OF TRIPE, A HALF GALLON OF PRUNE JUICE AND A LARGE PACK OF CHEEZ DOODLES.... I HAVEN'T SEEN HIM SINCE. "

CHARTER QUAHOGGER

" FRANCINE! HOW CAN YOU JUST SIT
THERE WITH ALL THAT DISGUSTING
BEHAVIOR GOING ON AT THE OTHER
END OF MOONSTONE BEACH?!"

VANITY PLATES
OF THE GODS

ⓣ OCEAN STATE
FOUNDA
RHODE ISLAND

ROGER WILLIAMS

ⓣ OCEAN STATE
THREDS
RHODE ISLAND

SAMUEL SLATER

ⓣ OCEAN STATE
FLY ME
RHODE ISLAND

THEODORE FRANCIS GREEN

...AND, IF 'SILENT CAL' COOLIDGE HAD BEEN A RHODE ISLANDER...

ⓣ OCEAN STATE

RHODE ISLAND

DON BOUSQUET

THE ORIGINAL
LOVE BOAT

DON BOUSQUET

"SAY, ISN'T THAT COMMODORE GNARPTH JUST BACK FROM FIVE YEARS OF INTERGALACTIC EXPLORATION?? WHO KNOWS WHAT STRANGE PLACES HE'S SEEN!"

" I UNDERSTAND THERE WAS A RUMOR
GOING AROUND IN THE 'SIXTIES THAT
FERNAND J. ST GERMAIN WAS REALLY
BATMAN — NOBODY EVER SAW THEM
TOGETHER AT THE SAME TIME . "

HOG ISLAND
STREET GANG MEMBER

" OH, LOOK, HOWARD, STEAMED CLAMS!
MY HOWARD HAS AN ALMOST UNNATURAL
FONDNESS FOR STEAMERS... "

" HEY, GRANPA...TELL ME AGAIN HOW
YOU RODE OUT HURRICANE CAROL IN
YOUR LOBSTER SKIFF ! "

BLOCK IS., RHODE ISLAND

GREAT MOMENTS
IN
RHODE ISLAND SHIPBUILDING HISTORY
78

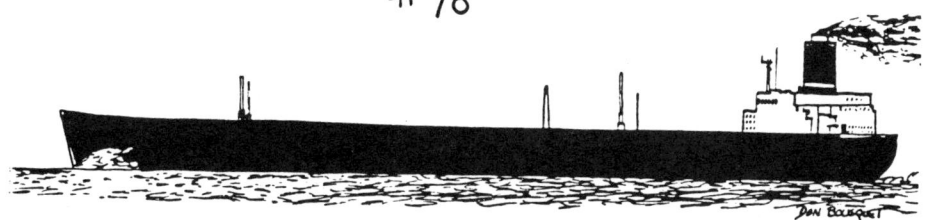

1980

THE SUPERTANKER, 'UNIVERSE FOLLICLE'
BECAME THE FIRST SHIP OVER 500,000
LONG TONS TO NAVIGATE THE POTOMAC.
IT TRANSPORTED 1.7 MILLION BARRELS
OF GRECIAN FORMULA, CALCULATED TO
BE SUFFICIENT FOR RONALD REAGAN'S
HAIR NEEDS DURING HIS FIRST TERM
OF OFFICE.

ADMIRING THE VIEW FROM THE
OBSERVATION DECK AT T. F. GREEN AIRPORT

ROCKY

NOOSENECK

BALD

WATCH

DON BOUSQUET

RHODE ISLAND: OUT TO LUNCH WHEN
THEY PASSED OUT THE MOUNTAIN RANGES
BUT WE'VE SURE GOT TERRIFIC HILLS!

" O.K. WHO'S THE MEATBALL AND
   PEPPER GRINDER AND WHO GETS
 THE FOIE DE VEAU LYONNAISE ? "

ARTIST'S CONCEPTION OF PROPOSED JAMESTOWN BRIDGE ENVISIONED BY REAGAN ADMINISTRATION

DON BOUSQUET

SCARBOROUGH BEACH
SNOWMAN

DON BOUSQUET

MOONSTONE BEACH
SNOWMAN

81

" OUR WEATHER CONTINUES TO BE
   DOMINATED BY A SLOW MOVING LOW
PRESSURE SYSTEM SWEEPING DOWN
   OUT OF CANADA..."

A BREAK IN THE TEDIUM OF
WINTERING ON BLOCK ISLAND

... AND WHILE YOU'RE OUT FILL UP THE CAR WITH GAS AND SWING BY THE MARKET AND PICK UP AT LEAST FOUR LOAVES OF BREAD AND ALL THE MILK YOU CAN CARRY AND BATTERIES, LOTS OF BATTERIES IN CASE THE POWER GOES OUT... I'LL FILL UP THE TUB 'CAUSE WE MIGHT LOSE THE WATER AND I'LL PUT THE KIDS AND THE DOG IN THE CELLAR... AND FIREWOOD, BRING IN AT LEAST HALF A CORD AND...

AVERAGE RHODE ISLAND FAMILY REACTING TO A FORECAST OF TWO TO FOUR INCHES OF SNOW

"SORRY, TURKEY'S ALL GONE BUT THERE'S A FINE EXTRA HELPING OF IMPORTED ENGLISH GRUEL FOR EVERYONE!"

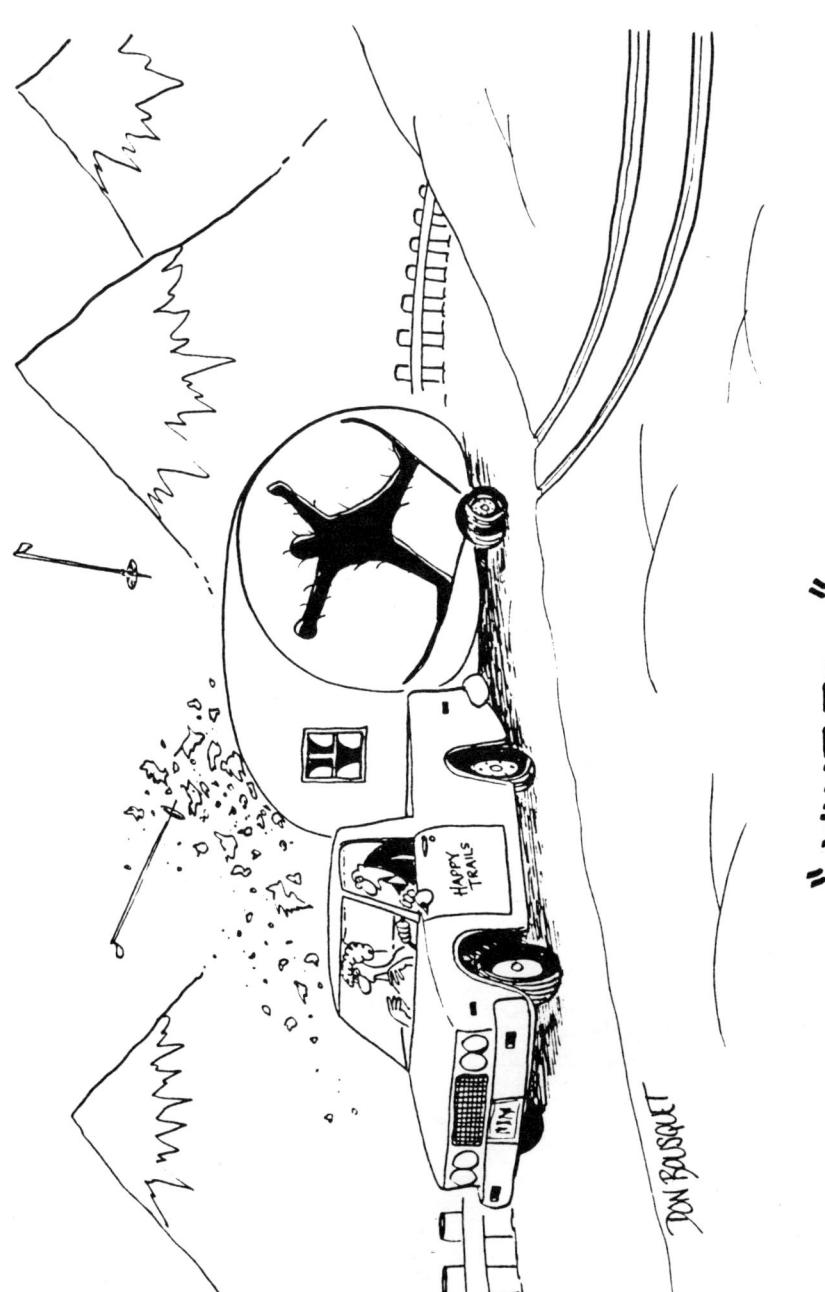

" WHAT TH... "

THE IMAGINATIVE RHODE ISLAND SHELLFISHERMAN CAN SAVE BIG MONEY ON DOCKING FEES BY PUTTING AN EXTRA SET OF QUAHOG TONGS TO GOOD USE.

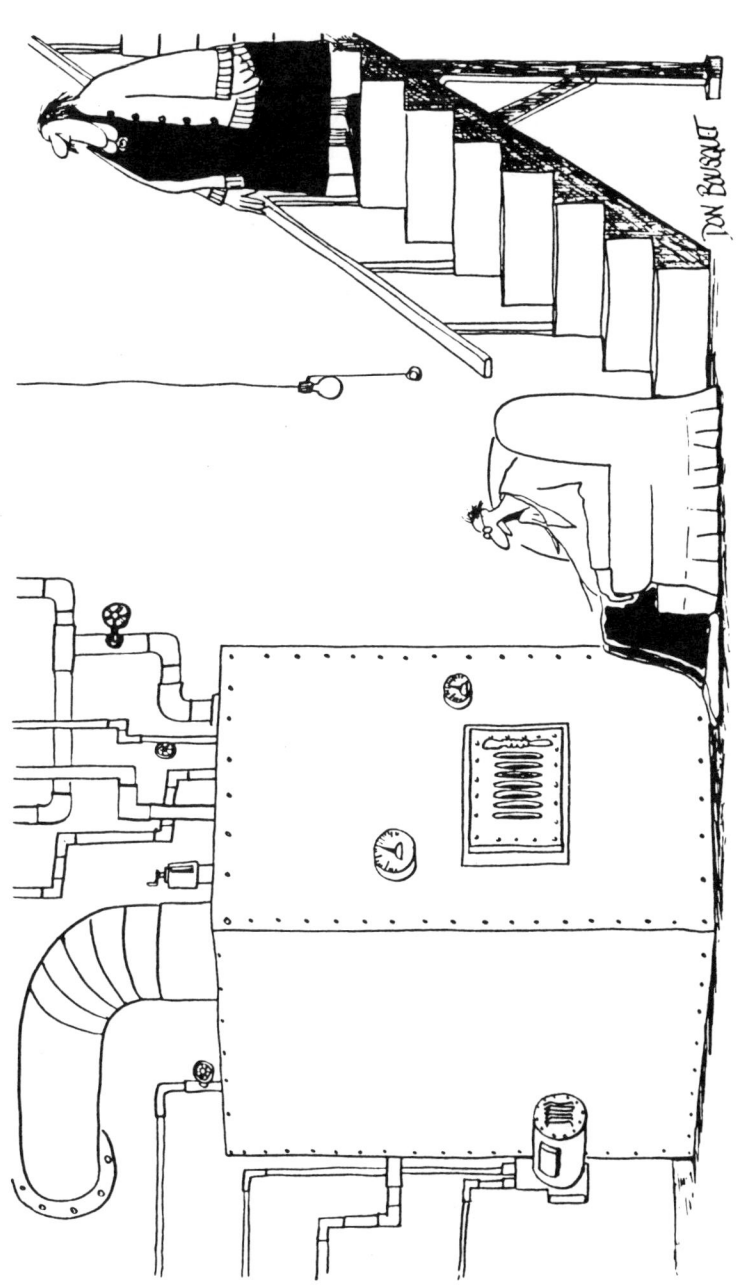

" BRITISH THERMAL UNITS, ALICE... BY GOD, THAT'S WHERE IT'S AT !"

" IT'S FROM MY AUNT KRISTEN BACK IN
RHODE ISLAND — A SIX MONTH SUPPLY
OF COFFEE SYRUP, ONE HUNDRED POUNDS
OF VERMICELLI AND A SET OF LOW NUMBER
R.I. DEALER PLATES!"

" THEN, AT ABOUT TWO A.M. YOU BROKE
INTO THE PETTING ZOO DOWN AT ROGER
WILLIAMS PARK AND SCREAMED, ' LET
MY PEOPLE GO! ' — BUT THAT'S NOT
QUITE ALL...."

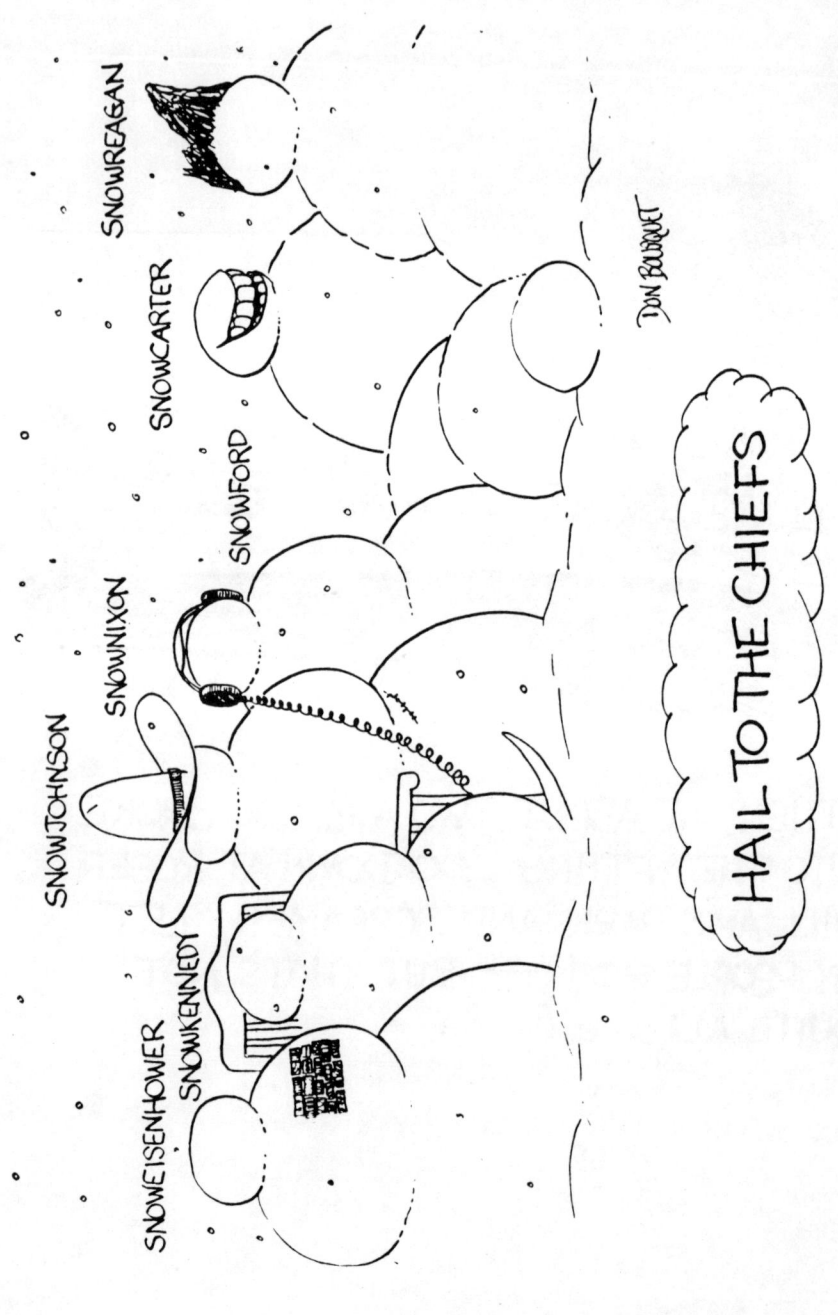

HAIL TO THE CHIEFS

94

"BY GOD, FENTON, THAT'S WHAT I CALL STATE-OF-THE-ART PASSIVE SOLAR TECHNOLOGY!"

" HELLO, HOUSTON... YOU'RE NOT GOING TO BELIEVE THIS... "

WHEN DINOSAURS ROAMED
RHODE ISLAND

The sign reads:

WOONSOCKET
POLICE
HEADQUARTERS

DON BOUSQUET

OCEAN STATE PICTURES
PRESENTS:
FILMED ON LOCATION IN
RHODE ISLAND,

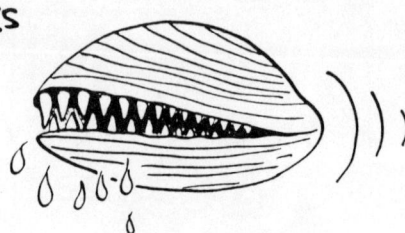

JUST WHEN YOU THOUGHT IT WAS SAFE
TO GO BACK TO FIELD'S POINT...

☆ STARRING ☆

MAXIMILIAN SCHELL, MEL BROOKS,
DINAH SHORE, EDDIE FISHER,
MUDDY WATERS, LLOYD BRIDGES
☆ SPECIAL GUEST APPEARANCE BY
JACQUES COUSTEAU AS
SENATOR CLAIBORNE PELL

DON BOUSQUET

100

SHIPWRECKED
In the Tunnel of Love

by Martha Smith
Maureen Croteau
Illustrated By Don Bousquet

$4.95

CLAMBAKE

How to Prepare a New England
Clambake — And More!

by W. Chris Heisler
Illustrated By Don Bousquet

$4.95

BE THE FIRST ON **YOUR** **DOCK** TO OWN A QUALITY QUAHOG T-SHIRT

"BELIEVE IT OR NOT, SOME GUY FROM RHODE ISLAND ORDERED A GRINDER AND A CABINET"

"TOO MUCH JUNKFOOD."

Please check shirt desired:

☐ **"Beware of the Quahog"**   ☐ **"Believe it or not..."**

☑ **"Too much junkfood."**   ☑ **"Born to Quahog."**

SIZE: S ☑   M ☐   L ☐   XL ☐

COLOR: White ☐   Blue ☑

PRICE: $6.95 + $1.25 Postage & Handling.

Please Send To: Mr./Mrs./Ms. _Fish_____

Recreation Publications P.O. Box 168 Wakefield, R.I. 02880

Address _____

City _____

State _____ Zip _____

HERE ARE **FOUR** GREAT WAYS TO
SEND DON BOUSQUET'S SPECIAL
BRAND OF HUMOR TO FRIENDS,
RELATIVES, DISPLACED RHODE
ISLANDERS, ETC. ANYWHERE IN
THE UNITED STATES.

1) *The Quahog Walks Among Us* — $3.95*
2) *Beware of the Quahog* — $3.95*
3) *I Brake for Quahogs* — $3.95*
4) *Bousquet Note Paper & Envelopes* — $3.95*

*Plus $1.50 Postage and Handling

ENCLOSED PLEASE FIND $_____

Please check: Quantity
☐ **The Quahog Walks Among Us**   _____
☐ **Beware of the Quahog**   _____
☐ **I Brake for Quahogs**   _____
☐ **Note Paper and Envelopes**   _____
Please send to:
Mr./Mrs./Ms. _____
Address _____
City _____ State _____ Zip _____

Recreation Publications
P.O. Box 168
Wakefield, R.I. 02880
401-789-3041